ON THE MOVE

A chronological study of vehicles from the Romans to modern times

Richard Dawson

MACMILLAN
CHILDREN'S BOOKS

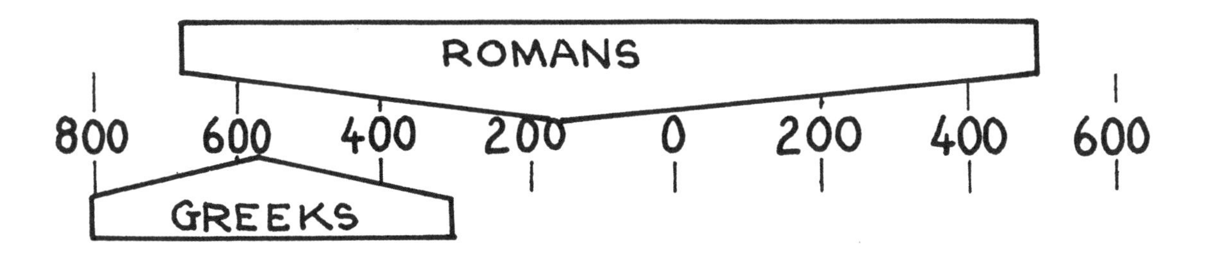

THE GREEKS

Although sea transport was very good during Greek times, land transport was very limited . . .

How do you think the Greek people got about?

Tick the transports they could have used.

Homer, a Greek poet, wrote a poem called the Iliad.

In the story Greek soldiers hid inside a huge wooden horse outside the besieged city of Troy. During the night the Trojans wondered what the horse was and moved it into the city. The Greeks then jumped out of the horse and captured Troy!

One soldier cannot find his way out.
Can you help him?

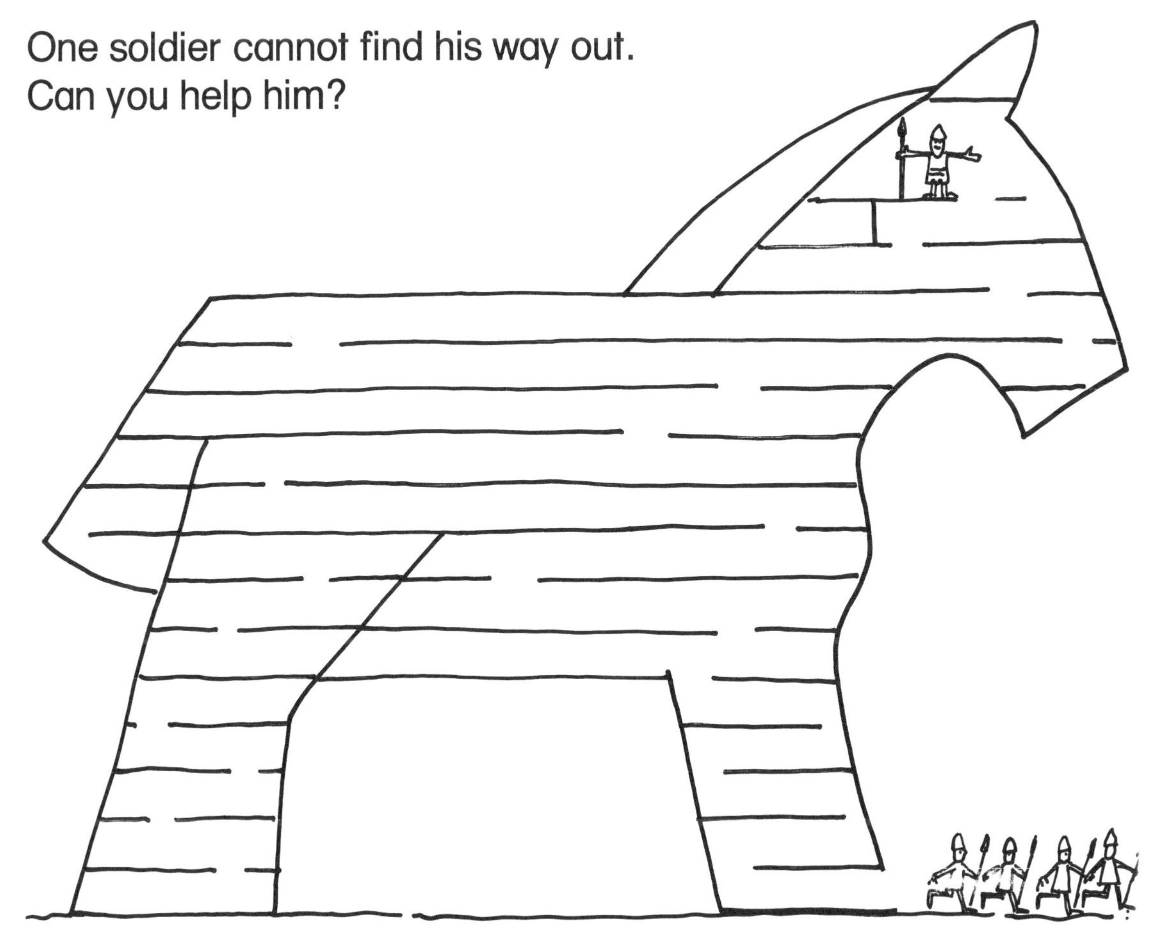

How do you think the Trojans moved the horse?

When Persia invaded Greece in 490 BC the Athenian Army, although greatly outnumbered, defeated them at the battle of Marathon. The Greeks were so delighted to have won the battle that they sent a message from Marathon to Athens 26 miles away. There was only one way for the messenger to travel and that was on foot!

The messenger ran so hard, without stopping, that after delivering the news of the victory to the people of Athens, he collapsed and died!

We have a Marathon race in athletics now . . . is this longer or shorter than the first Marathon run?

A Greek horseman

A modern horseman

Circle the differences.

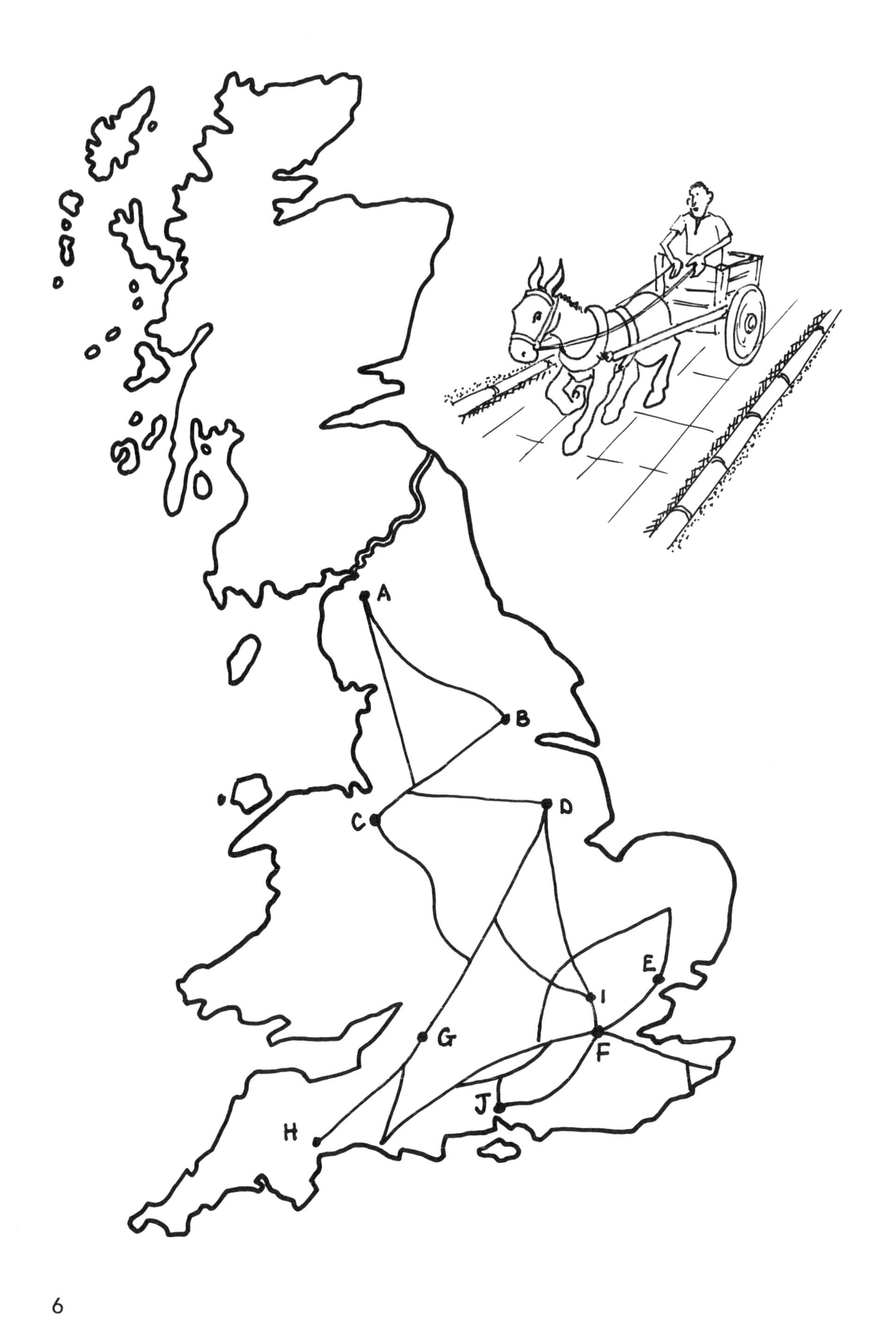
A
B
C
D
E
I
F
G
J
H

The Romans

The Romans were great road builders. They built roads to move their armies around the countries they conquered.

Can you link the names of the Roman towns to the letters shown on the map?

______	Exeter	______	Southampton
______	Bath	______	London
______	York	______	Carlisle
______	Lincoln	______	Chester
______	St Albans	______	Colchester

What do you notice about the roads?

____

What methods of transport do you think the Romans used?

____

____

The Romans put stones every thousand paces. These were the first mile stones! The Roman word for thousand was *mille*. The monks who maintained the roads would have kept the mile stones, and later a mile became a unit of measurement, but was longer than 1000 paces!

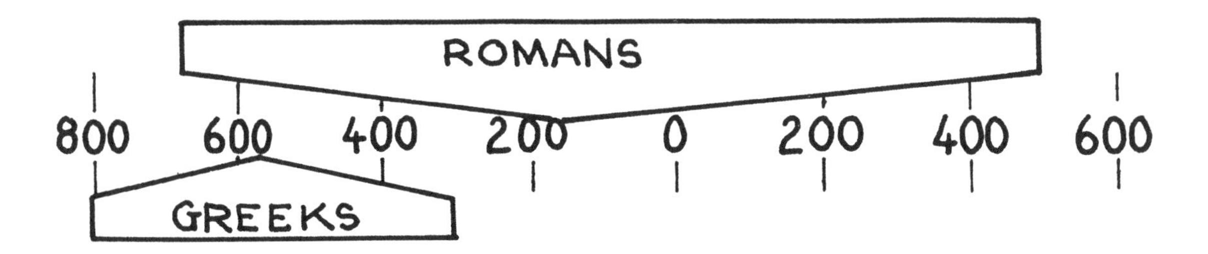

THE VIKINGS

The Viking lands were rocky and the winters were long and cold with lots of snow. Vikings designed new and different kinds of transport to get over the snow (see page 10) but horses and oxen remained the power source.

One development of some Danish Vikings was to put roller bearings in wagon wheels.

How do you think they worked?

____

____

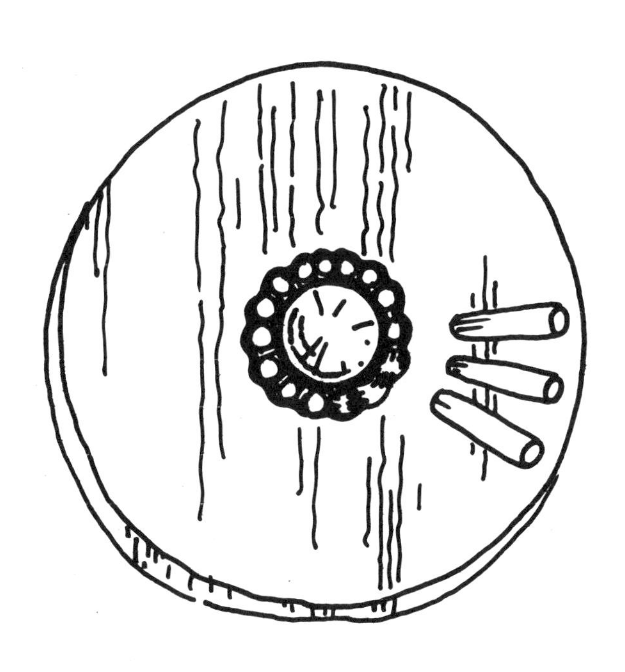

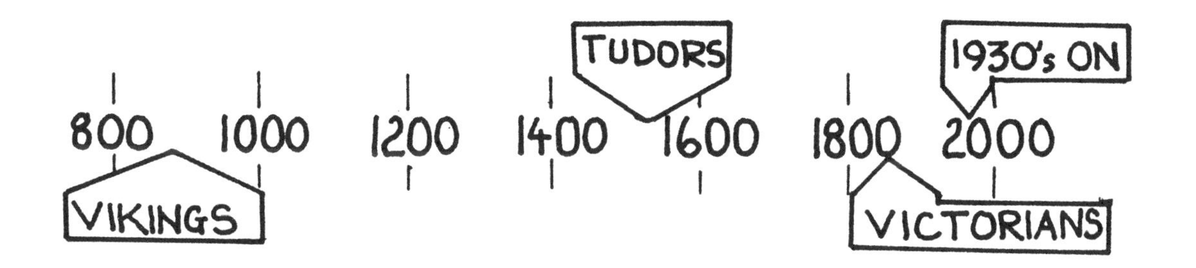

Which of these wheels might the Vikings have used on their carts?

Viking snow travel

What did the Vikings use? There are clues in the picture!

Erik has lost a wagon wheel. Which is the shortest route to the bottom of the Runic path? Mind the logs!

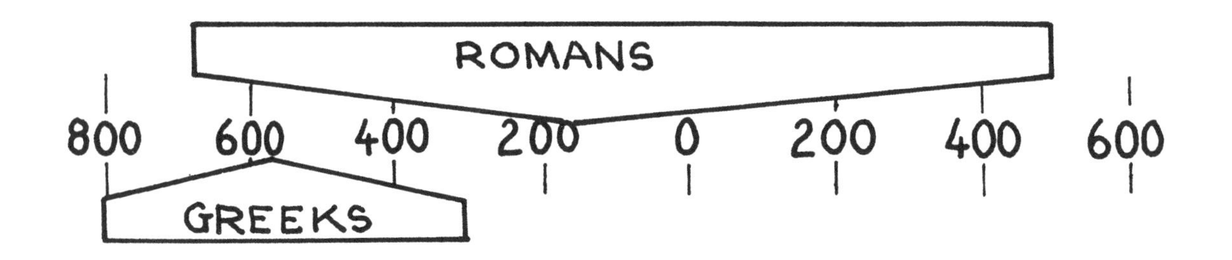

THE ELIZABETHANS

The Roman roads had been maintained by monks during the Middle Ages, but after Queen Elizabeth's father, Henry VIII, closed most of the monasteries, the roads soon fell into disrepair.

In summer the hard surface made travelling very bumpy and in winter the mud made travel almost impossible. The heavy wagons cut ruts up to a metre deep, filled with rain water these became a very dangerous hazard!

There were no sign posts or milestones, and lots of people got lost. Travellers were often in danger from robbers who hid in the trees and bushes at the roadside.

Queen Elizabeth left London to spend the summer in the country . . . Her luggage and household had to be transported in 400 six-horse carts! How many horses is that?

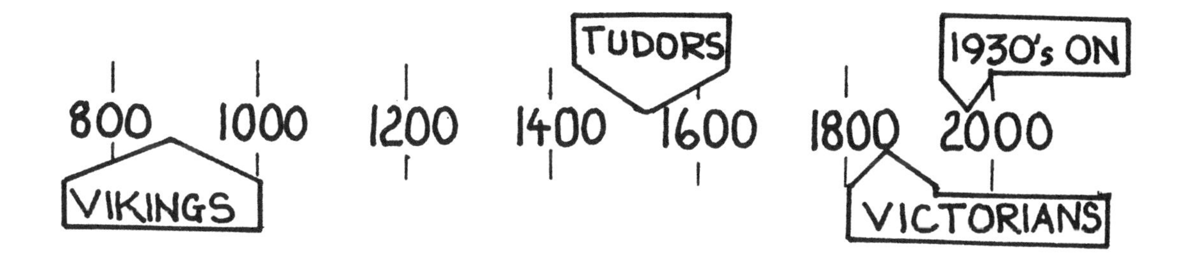

As the roads were in a poor state, pack horses were used to carry goods to London. Which of these things were taken to London by pack horse during Elizabethan times?

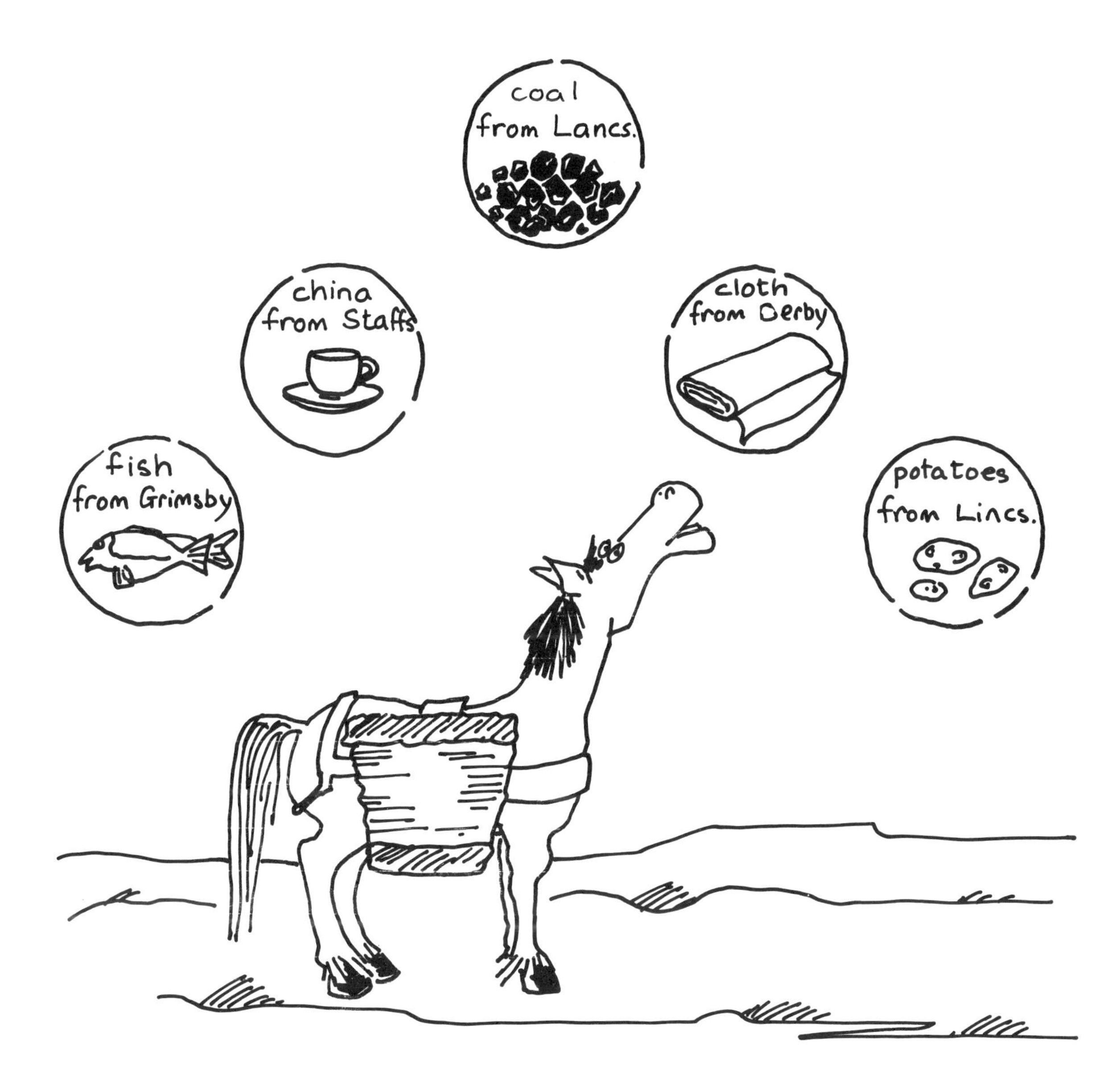

Colour in Queen Elizabeth's favourite method of transport.

Travelling long distance was a problem. Rich people rode on horseback. It would take up to five days to travel from London to Edinburgh. Travellers were able to exchange horses every 10 miles at inns. One man who hired out horses kept a stable of forty. When someone wanted to hire a horse they were given the horse nearest the stable door. The man's name was Thomas Hobson and those who hired his horses got Hobson's choice!

What does Hobson's choice mean today?

____

____

Letters were carried by messengers on horseback. Henry VIII, Elizabeth's father, decided to set up a special delivery service for his letters called the Royal Mail. A man called Brian Tuke was appointed to organize the delivery of the Royal Mail. He divided roads up so that every 12½ miles there was an inn where the messengers could change their horses and have a meal. He called these halts 'posts'. The messengers became known as 'post boys'. Although they do not ride horses today we still have ______________ .

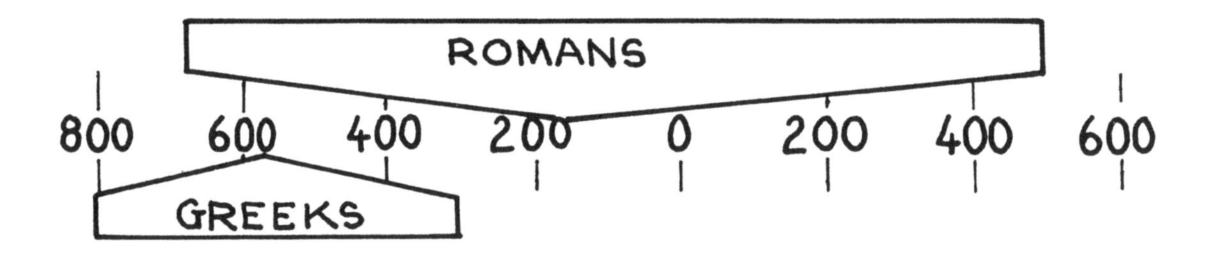

The Victorians

When Queen Victoria was a child there were only two ways of travelling – walking and on horseback. By the end of Queen Victoria's reign she could travel by tram, train, tube or even motor car!

When Queen Victoria was a girl, how did she travel?

Colour in the correct pictures.

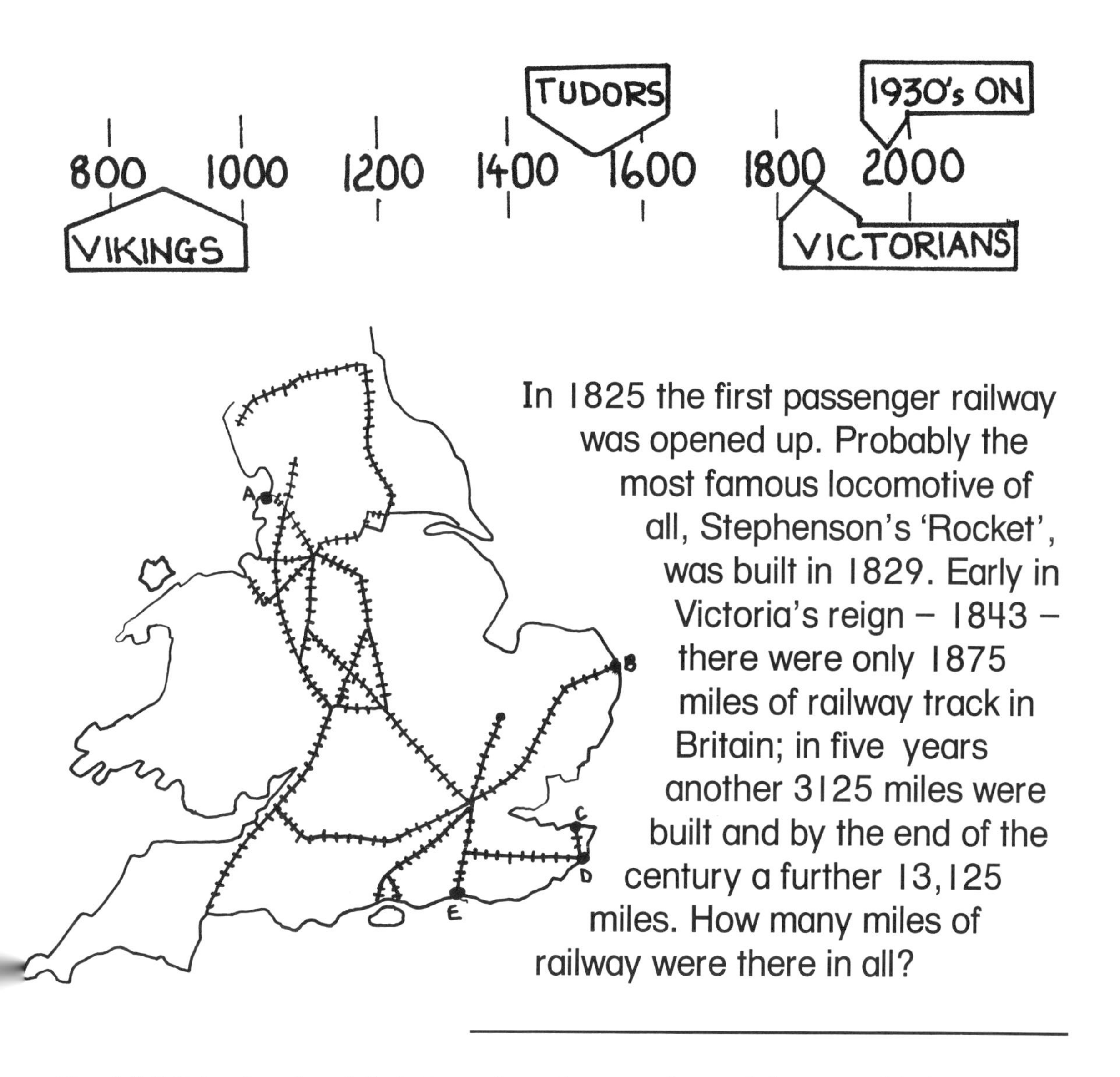

In 1825 the first passenger railway was opened up. Probably the most famous locomotive of all, Stephenson's 'Rocket', was built in 1829. Early in Victoria's reign – 1843 – there were only 1875 miles of railway track in Britain; in five years another 3125 miles were built and by the end of the century a further 13,125 miles. How many miles of railway were there in all?

____

By 1880 trains had lighting, heating and corridors and it became very fashionable to take holidays.

Use a map to find the favourite holiday spots.

A ____________________

B ____________________

C ____________________

D ____________________

E ____________________

When were these trains running?

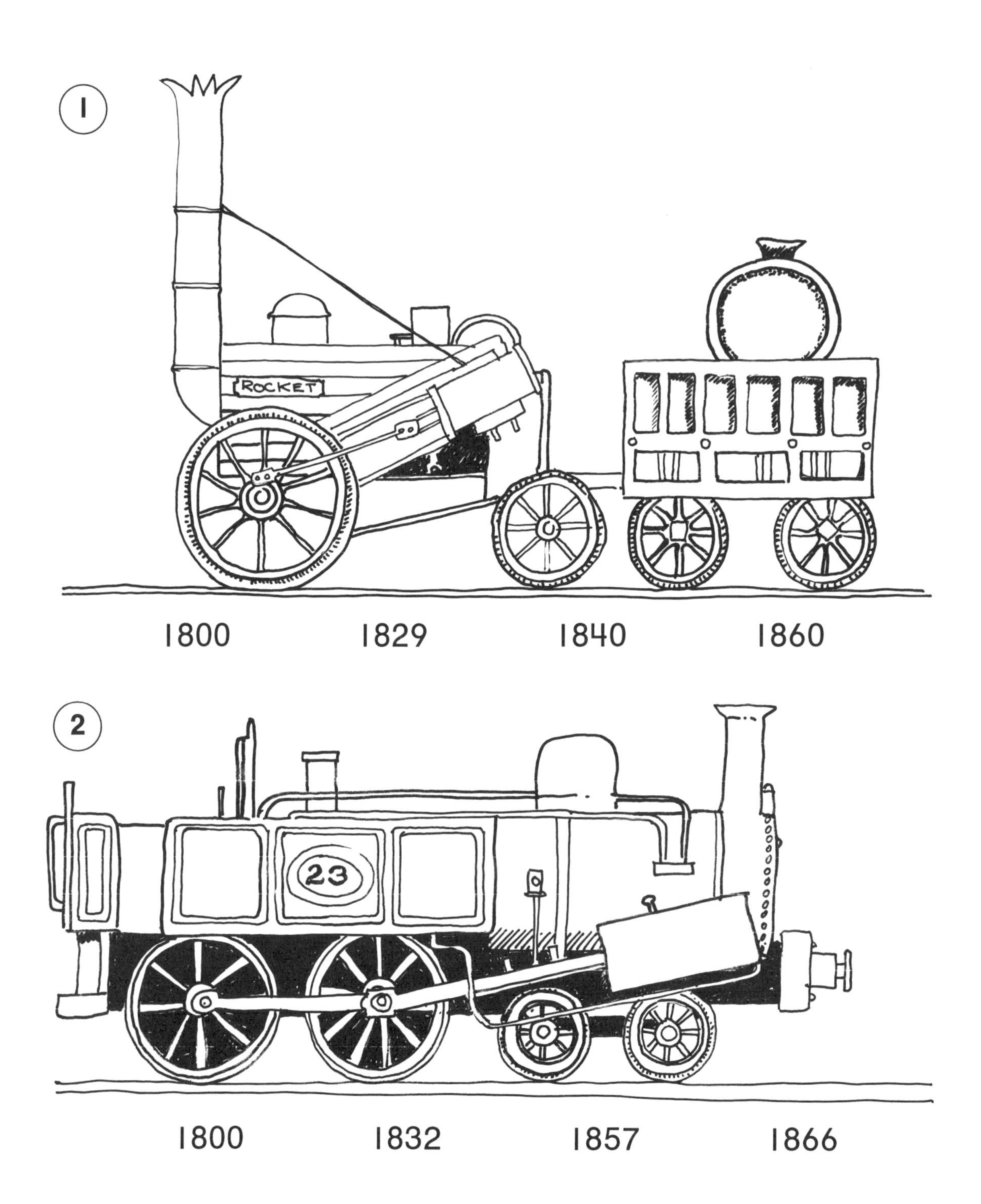

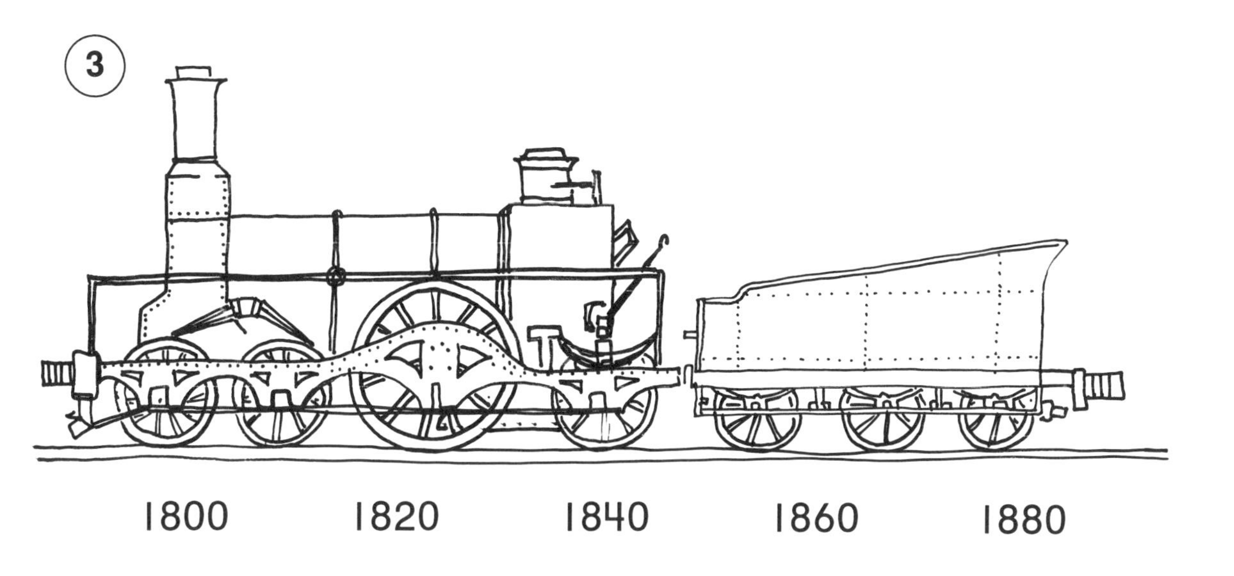

Thomas Cook hired a train in 1841 to take 570 people to a lecture about the evils of drinking. His excursion was very successful and Mr Cook began organizing train journeys all over the country.

His fares were within the reaches of the working classes. By the 1870s Thomas Cook was arranging holidays to places as far away as Egypt!

An organization called Thomas Cook still exists today . . . Where can you holiday now with Thomas Cook?

A journey from Manchester to London took four and a half days by horse-drawn coach but by the 1840s a train could make the journey in twelve hours.

While the train replaced the long distance coach in Victorian times, horse-drawn vehicles were still a most popular transport.

How many wheels did each of these carriages have?
And how many horses pulled each?

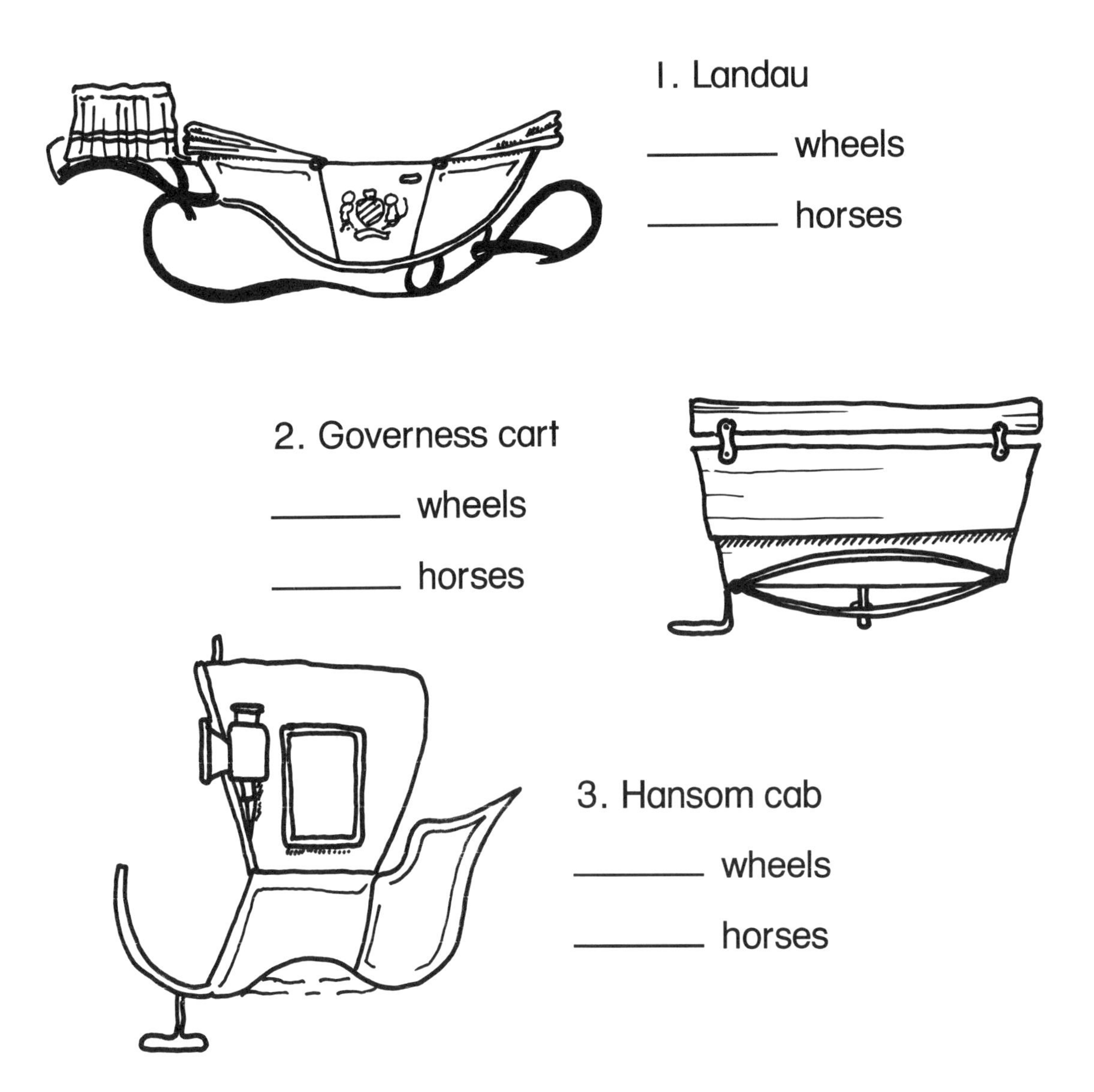

1. Landau

_______ wheels

_______ horses

2. Governess cart

_______ wheels

_______ horses

3. Hansom cab

_______ wheels

_______ horses

Which of these carriages were pulled by horses?
Colour them in.

Cycling became a very popular form of transport in Victorian times.

The penny-farthing, invented in 1870 by James Starley, was probably the best known of all old cycles.

How do you think it got its name?

The front wheel was nearly two metres in diameter and the only way of stopping was by back pedalling! Great skill was needed to actually get on a penny-farthing, and downhill travel was particularly dangerous as there was always a chance of flying over the handlebars!

Move the book in a circular motion. What seems to happen to the wheels?

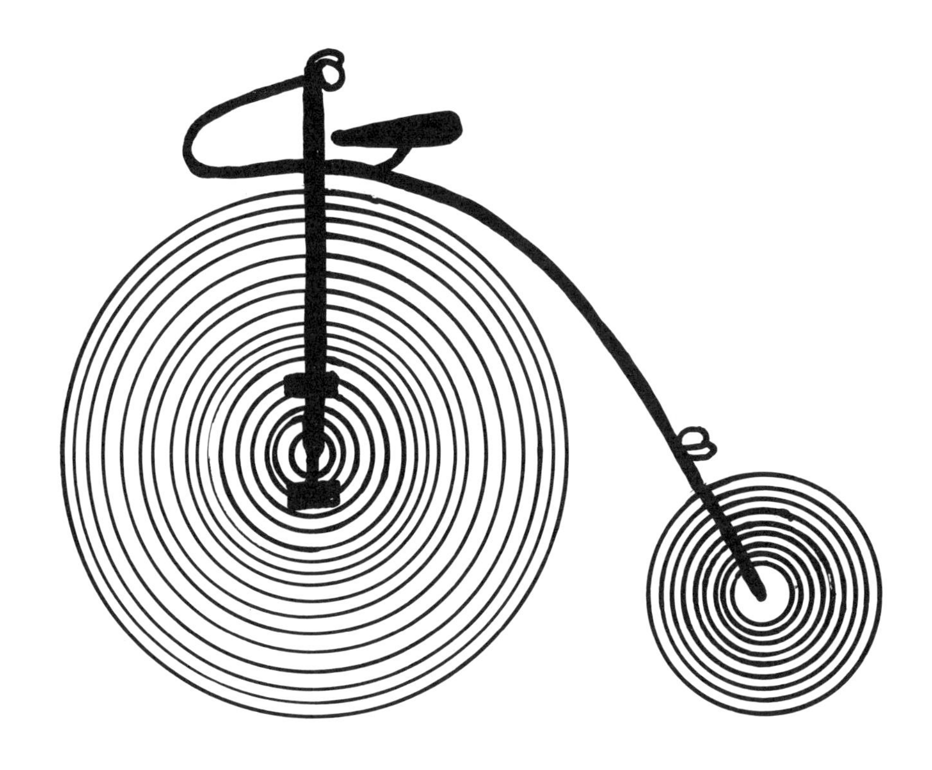

Until 1888 bicycles bounced along on solid rubber tyres; no wonder they were called boneshakers! Then a vet called John Dunlop invented and patented the pneumatic tyre. This was one of the most important inventions for cycles and indeed for all modern road vehicles.

Find your way along the tyre maze from the valve to the puncture.

On Your Bike!

During the 1870s cyclists and horse riders began falling out! Cyclists were known as 'scorchers'. Dogs were set on them, sticks were poked through cycle wheels and even wires were stretched across roads! . . . all because cycles travelled too fast!

Coaches travelled between London and Brighton until 1890. In 1888 the record for the journey was broken . . . it took seven hours and fifty minutes. To make this record James Selby used thirteen teams of four horses . . . the quickest change was forty-seven seconds.

In 1890 this record was broken by a cyclist – using the new pneumatic tyres. His journey took seven hours and nineteen minutes.

This record has been broken on cycles many times since. The current record for the 106 miles is four hours and thirteen minutes. Use your calculator to work out how many miles per hour each was travelling.

Many people were now getting about on bicycles and the next form of transport to develop was the . . .

. . . motor car! This car, designed by Karl Benz, was built in 1885 and had a top speed of 7 ½ miles per hour!

What is the main difference between Karl Benz's car and all modern cars?

____

Many roads had now been rebuilt by the famous road makers called Telford and Macadam. However all the extra traffic on the roads, especially those with the pneumatic tyres, were ripping up the stones in the Macadam roads. It was discovered that by pouring tar over the surface and rolling it a much better surface was made.

What do you think the new surface was called? It has the same name today!

____

A Victorian Crossword

1 & 2 A horseless carriage
3 Town travel for lots of people
4 Pedal Power!
5 One big wheel, one small
6 Pulled by horse and train
7 The Victorian invention that opened up the country
8 Buses on rails
9 A governess _ _ _ _
10 The original power source

How would they have moved the block of stone?

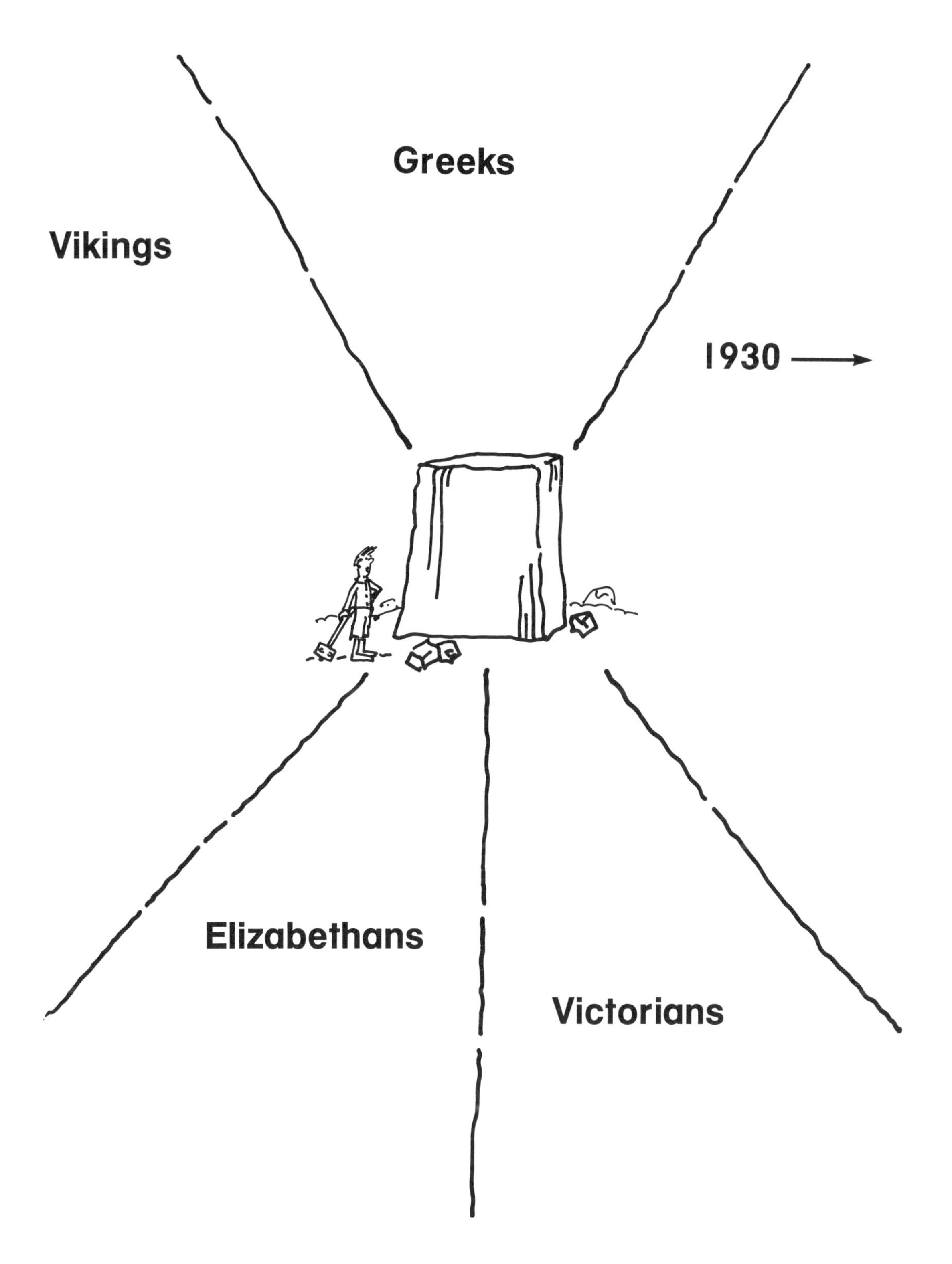

THE 1930S ONWARDS

During the war years petrol was on ration. What fuel was used instead of petrol?

____

During the war years sign posts were removed.
Why? ______________________________________

Which cars had these badges?

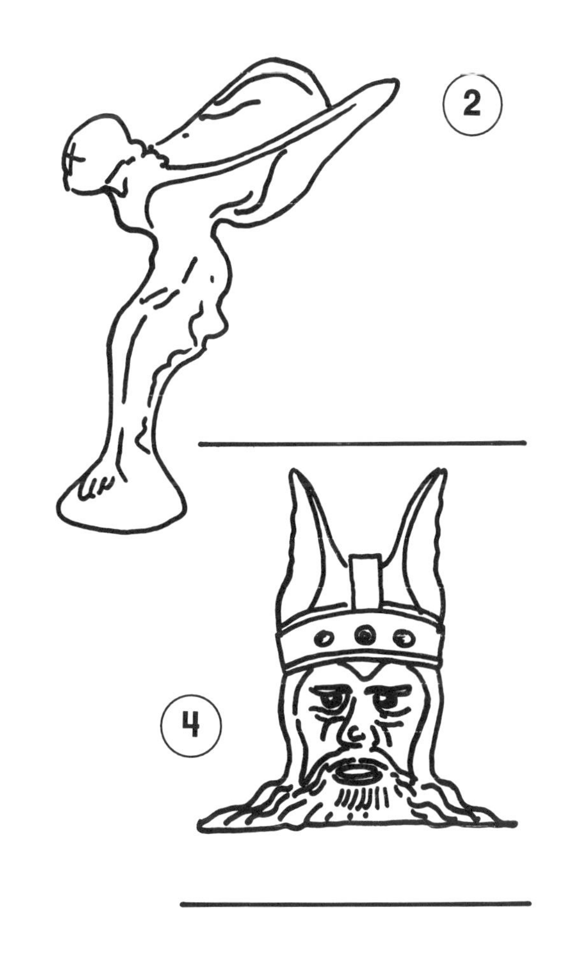

Fun Wheels

Draw all the wheels you can think of . . .

A car of the future?

Design your own futuristic car here . . .

What fuels might cars run on in the future?

Answers

page 2 Donkey, feet, chariot, horse

page 3 On wheels

page 4 A modern marathon is 26 miles and 385 yards (42.195 km). This is the distance from the gates of Windsor Great Park to the Olympic Stadium in London. This distance was established during the 1908 Olympics.

page 5 There are no saddle or stirrups on the Greek horseman.

page 7 A. Carlisle, B. York, C. Chester, D. Lincoln, E. Colchester, F. London, G. Bath, H. Exeter, I. St Albans, J. Southampton

page 8 The rollers turned as the wheel moved on the axle, reducing friction and keeping the wheel from sticking.

page 9 All except 3. page 12. 2,400 horses.

page 13 Everything except potatoes.

page 14 Horseback. After travelling by state coach (which was invented for Elizabeth) she complained about the bruises!

page 15 Hobson's Choice is no choice! We still have postmen.

page 16 3. Horse and cart.

page 17 There were 18,125 miles of railway in all.
A.Blackpool, B.Gt Yarmouth, C.Margate, D.Ramsgate, E.Brighton

page 18 1. 1829, 2. 1866, 3. 1840.

page 19 Look in a Thomas Cook brochure; you can go almost anywhere in the world!

page 20 1. 4 wheels, 2 horses, 2. 2 wheels, 1 horse (pony!), 3. 2 wheels (for quick turning in towns and cities), 1 horse.

page 21 A. Steam carriage, B. Train, C. Train, D. Horse, E. Horse, F. Horse.

page 22 After the coins: penny (large) and farthing (small).

page 24 13.5 mph, 14.5 mph, 25 mph

page 25 Steering wheel. Tarmac(adam)

page 26 1. Motor, 2. Car, 3. Omnibus, 4. Bicycle, 5. Penny Farthing, 6. Carriage, 7. Railway, 8. Tram, 9. Cart, 10. Horse

page 27 Greeks...a crane. Vikings...rollers. Elizabethans...rollers and horses. Victorians...a crane. 1930 → ...helicopter.

page 28 Gas was used instead of petrol. Signposts were removed to confuse the enemy if they landed!

page 29 1. Morris, 2. Rolls-Royce, 3. Ferrari, 4. Rover, 5. Austin.

First published 1995 by Macmillan Children's Books, a division of Macmillan General Books Ltd
Cavaye Place London SW10 9PG and Basingstoke
Associated companies throughout the world

ISBN 0 330 33391 7

9 8 7 6 5 4 3 2 1

A CIP catalogue record for this book is available from the British Library.

Printed and bound in Great Britain by Henry Ling Ltd, The Dorset Press, Dorchester